Y0-BZI-747

Table of Contents

Phonics Reader 13: *This Is Fun!*

Phonics Reader 14: *The Big Nut*

Phonics Reader 15: *Rob's Shop*

Assessment: Phonics Readers 13–15

Workbook

5

Listen. Read. Write.
Consonant

S s

Trace the capital and small letter Ss. Write the letter.

Color the pictures whose names have the sound of **z** as in **cheese**.
Write **Ss** next to those pictures.

You use this [   ] to smell this. [   ]

Circle the pictures in each row whose names have the sound of **z** as in **cheese**.

I am a yellow-and-white flower.
My name has the sound of **z**
as in **cheese**. What am I?

Listen. Read. Write. Consonant

Trace the capital and small letter Yy. Write the letter.

Which picture names begin with the sound of **y** as in **yo-yo**? Write **Yy** under those pictures.

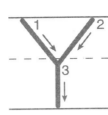

Can you solve these riddles? Both answers have the sound of **y**.

You do this when you are sleepy.

You do this at a football game.

One of the words names the picture.
Underline the words that have the sound
of **-in** as in **chin**.
Write it on the lines.

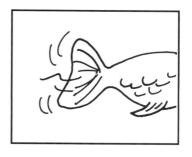

fin, fit _____

win, run _____

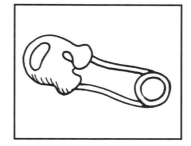

pan, pin _____

twins, tents _____

Put something on
my face to show
I am happy.

Hint: it's a sticker
with the **-in** sound.

Phonics Reader 13: *This Is Fun!*

5

Let's Review s, y, -in

Underline the word that has a sound or sounds that are also in the picture name.

his, him, hat

fun, fed, frogs

jazz, wet, yes

suds, rock, pot

six, you, was

legs, lost, stuff

sock, can, skin

sees, flop, hop

rut, trees, big

yell, will, up

pot, bed, pin

What is the opposite of thick?

What do you call 365 days?

Use one of these words to finish each sentence

each   if   some   use   your

1. He has _____ gum.

2. Can I pet _____ cat?

3. We will _____ a pot for the plant.

4. Dan and Bud _____ have a bat.

5. You will win _____ you run fast.

These pictures from *This* Is *Fun!* show what the family did in Fun Land.
Answer each question with a word that tells about the picture.
The answers have the sounds of **-in** or **y**.

What does Min do in the cup?

_____

- - - - - - - - - - - - - -

_____

What do they do?

_____

- - - - - - - - - - - - - -

_____

What does Min do with the fin?

_____

- - - - - - - - - - - - - -

_____

What does Min do when
she gets her pet?

_____

- - - - - - - - - - - - - -

_____

V v

Trace the capital and small letter Vv. Write the letter.

Which picture names begin with the sound of **v** as in **vest**?
Write **Vv** under those pictures.

Can you find something that grows whose name begins with the **v** sound?

QU, qu

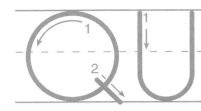

Trace the capital and small letters QU, qu. Write the letters.

Color the pictures whose names start with the sound of **qu** as in **quilt**. Write **QU qu** below those pictures.

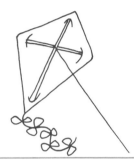

Ssh! The baby is asleep. What should we be?

Find the **qu** answer on the sticker page.

Write the letters ut under the pictures whose names end with the sounds of **-ut** as in **nut**.

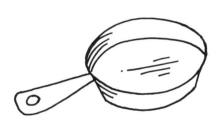

_____

- - - - - - - - - - - - - -

_____

_____

- - - - - - - - - - - - - -

_____

_____

- - - - - - - - - - - - - -

_____

_____

- - - - - - - - - - - - - -

_____

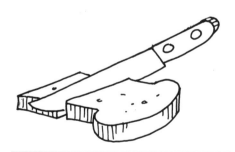

_____

- - - - - - - - - - - - - -

_____

_____

- - - - - - - - - - - - - -

_____

the door! It's cold outside.
Hint: the answer has the
end sound of -**ut**.

Let's Review v, qu, -ut

Say the name of each picture.
Make an x in the box that has one of the sounds you hear.

❏ v
❏ qu
❏ ut

❏ v
❏ qu
❏ ut

❏ v
❏ qu
❏ ut

❏ v
❏ qu
❏ ut

❏ v
❏ qu
❏ ut

❏ v
❏ qu
❏ ut

❏ v
❏ qu
❏ ut

❏ v
❏ qu
❏ ut

❏ v
❏ qu
❏ ut

❏ v
❏ qu
❏ ut

❏ v
❏ qu
❏ ut

❏ v
❏ qu
❏ ut

Listen. Read. Write. Words to Remember:
do, how, into, these, would

Use one of these words to finish each sentence.

do   how   into   these   would

"I will go _____ the pond."

"_____ you like to race?

"Yes. I _____ like to race with you."

"_____ can you hop so fast?"

"_____ legs are long."

Phonics Reader 14: *The Big Nut*

13

Think about the story you read called *The Big Nut*.
Draw a picture of what happens next in the story.

Write **ob** to finish each word.
Draw a line to match each word
with its picture.

s l _____

j _____

s _____

c _____

Bob has a friend whose name
also ends with the sound of **-ob**.
Who is it?

Make new **ob** words. Write the words.

Change the at in **sat** to ob. _____

Change the ig in **jig** to ob. _____

Change the ad in **glad** to ob. _____

Change the t in **rot** to b. _____

s h

Write **sh** under the pictures whose names begin with the sound of **sh** as in **shoe**.

_____

- - - - - - - -

_____

- - - - - - - -

_____

- - - - - - - -

_____

- - - - - - - -

_____

- - - - - - - -

_____

- - - - - - - -

Can you find these **sh** stickers?

I found a [ ] on the beach.

I put it on a [ ] in my room.

Listen. Read. Write. Digraph

sh

Solve the puzzle.
Color all the pieces that end with
the sound of **sh** as in **wash**.

Can you find the **sh** stickers that finish this sentence?

If you spill
something
on your

, you have to

it.

Look at the picture. Write the missing letters to finish the picture name.

_____ o r t s   b r u _____   c _____

s _____   _____ i p   b u _____

My name starts with **sh**. You can dig with me.

I help open doors. I have the sound of **ob** in my name.

Use these words to finish the sentence.

could   look   make   more   than

He has more jam _____ me.

Would you like some _____ jam?

Bob will _____ a hat for Jan.

She _____ not get the hat on.

"How do I _____ ?" she said.

The pictures from the story *Rob's Shop* are out of order.
Put them in story order by writing 1, 2, 3, or 4 under each picture.

_____

- - - - - - -

_____

_____

- - - - - - -

_____

_____

- - - - - - -

_____

Fill in the circle next to the word that best finishes each sentence.
Write the word on the line.

1.

She _____ the cat.

○ sit, ○ sees, ○ sad

2.

He ate a _____ .

○ nut, ○ nip, ○ nap

3.

We will _____ the race.

○ wet, ○ web, ○ win

4.

My Mom said _____ .

○ shop, ○ her, ○ yes

5.

He is in a _____ .

○ hut, ○ bed, ○ van

6.

The ducks said, "_____ ."

○ hi, ○ Quack, ○ yes

Test Yourself!

Underline the word that names each picture.
Then write the word on the line.

1. This top can _____ .
   hop, spin, run

2. Dad has on a _____ .
   hat, mitt, vest

3. Nan will go to her _____ .
   job, bed, den

4. Look at the _____ .
   dogs, cats, sheep

5. He will _____ at the pup.
   fill, yell, mill

6. She has some jam on her _____ .
   leg, dish, cup

Answer Key

PAGE 2   hose, eyes, birds

PAGE 3   bees, toes, dogs

knees, bows, peas

shoes, eggs, cars

skis, trees, pies

PAGE 4   yolk, yard, yarn

PAGE 5   fin, win, pin, twins

PAGE 6   his, frogs, yes, suds, you, legs,

skin, sees, trees, yell, pin

PAGE 7   some, your, use, each, if

PAGE 8   spin, yell, pin, grin

PAGE 9   vase, violin, valentine

PAGE 10   queen, quarter, question

PAGE 11   hut, cut

PAGE 12   qu, v, qu, v

v, ut, qu, v

qu, ut, v, ut

PAGE 13   into, Do, would, How, These

PAGE 14   Duck's beak is stuck in the nut.

PAGE 15   slob, job, sob, cob

PAGE 16   sob, job, glob, rob

PAGE 17   shirt, ship, sheep

PAGE 18   leash, dish, fish, brush

PAGE 19   shorts, brush, cob, sob, ship, bush

PAGE 20   than, more, make, could, look

PAGE 21   2, 4, 1, 3 (left to right, top to bottom)

PAGE 22   1. sees

2. nut

3. win

4. yes

5. van

6. Quack

PAGE 23   1. spin

2. vest

3. job

4. sheep

5. yell

6. dish